Dedicated to my daughter Sue.

Honouring the forerunners . . .

Ian Clayton (Son of Thunder Ministry) It began for me in Coeur D'alene, Idaho, at a conference where Ian taught us to 'step in – step out' How simple; yet, so profound! Then, I took his advice "Get the CD" and now for years have listened to literally hundreds of hours of his great teachings! Heaven has become my home – I no longer just hope to 'see. It is real and now all I know is that I have so much more to learn.

Kathy Madden (Heaven's Call) Kathy helped me to experience the wonderful world of the Kingdom of Heaven through adventures beyond my understanding. I found out most importantly that we learn more about a place by visiting it than reading about it in books. Such a powerful truth!

Justin Abraham (Company of Burning Hearts) His podcasts excited me and spurred me on to understand and engage in the New Creation Reality we are to live and so much more! The JOY in the journey is the hallmark of Justin's teachings – totally out of this world!

Grant and Sam Mahoney (Ohel Moed) This couple model and live their life beyond the veil. They teach simply and so clearly that we can walk stronger, fly higher, and help others to journey as well. Along with Ian Clayton, they host an amazing on line training called THE NEST. You will be forever changed taking this course.

Mike Parsons (Freedom ARC) Mike takes the complex, makes it simple and helps us engage and activate our faith each time taking us deeper and higher at the same time.

There are many more folk who are paving a way to greater intimacy with the Lord. If you are reading this book ... one of those pioneers is YOU!

Thank you all so much!

With love – forever and always, Helen

Jacob's Ladder

Kingdom Adventures with Jake and Jenny

Story and Illustrations by: Helen Toews

Layout and Design by: Robert Connor

Scripture verses: New King James Version (NKJV), New American Standard Bible (NASB), New Living Translation (NLT), New International Version (NIV)

ISBN 978-0-9781724-1-1 Copyright Cottage at Creek Bend 2017
Author may be contacted by e-mail: cottage@mymts.net

Jake and Jenny were twins.

Jake had bragging rights to being the 'oldest' but as Jenny would remind him often, "You are only older by 5 minutes and that doesn't make you any smarter!"

They would often make fun of each other especially about Jake being 'older' but the fact was that they were the very best of friends.

Jake and Jenny shared a nursery ever since they were born. Their mom said that maybe it was time to have their own rooms but, both of them liked sharing a room and being together even though they were almost six and learning to read.

They were as different as day and night. Even their bunk beds had their personal touch.

Jake was always running and jumping. Jenny liked to be more quiet and thoughtful.

Every night Jake and Jenny would kneel by their beds. One would begin to pray and the other would continue, sometimes finishing the other's sentence - as twins will often do.

"Heavenly Father" Jake would pray, "Thank you for our family." Jenny would then say, "Thank you for looking after us every day..." Bless Daddy, Mommy and Grandpa . . ."Jake would then say, "And Lord, don't forget Grandma too."

They continued in this manner until, together they would say "AMEN" really loudly.

One evening Jake and Jenny watched a movie with their Mom and Dad. It was called "Heaven is for Real".

They all loved popcorn and movie nights.
Everyone loves popcorn. . . .

Especially
Jake!

After the movie, Jenny jumped into bed and asked, "Jake, what do you think heaven is like?"

"Well, the boy in the movie saw some people that he knew there. He saw his grandfather and his sister. It sure seemed like a real place." Jake replied.

Thoughtfully Jenny said, "Miss Marlene at Sunday School says that Jesus told His disciples "The Kingdom of Heaven is at hand."

"She says that means when you hold your hand up to your face and feel the warmth, that's how close heaven is. Hmmm. . . Miss Marlene must know a lot about God."

"Repent for the kingdom of heaven is at hand." Matthew 3:2 (NJKV)

Afterwards, the twins laid in their beds without talking for a long time. They were both looking up at the ceiling. They were thinking about heaven.

Set your mind on things above, not on things of the earth. Colossian 3:2 (NKJV)

"Remember the story of Jacob in the Bible?" Jenny asked.

"Yes of course!" Jake replied. "He's the guy that
went up the ladder. He has my name - Jacob.
I wonder if his dad called him Jake too?"

Then, rather sheepishly, Jake said, "When I imagine the story I can
see it. It is like a movie in my mind. I can see the angels going up
and coming down, just like in the story Miss Marlene reads us."

"Oh Jake, sometimes I do that too!" Jenny said excitedly.
"Lets imagine together."

That night Jenny and Jake said another prayer. "Heavenly Father,
could you show us heaven like you did for the boy in the movie?"

And, he said to him, "Most assuredly, I say to you, hereafter you shall see heaven open, and
the angels of God ascending and descending upon the Son of Man." John 1:51 (NKJV)

They both laid their heads on their pillows and were very quiet. They imagined a ladder that reached from their beds right into the sky. It seemed to go up, and up, and up!

"Oh my," Jenny said quietly. "I can really see angels and it looks like a long staircase."

"Me too," said Jake. "I'm going to go up!"

"If you are going, I'm going too!" Jenny smiled as she saw the stairs that reached right through the clouds.

"I can see a gate at the top Jenny. Do you see it?"

Jake was surprised but then Jenny said, "Yes I can, and I see a person there, waiting for us to come up."

On the way up the stairs Jenny and Jake looked closely at the angels. They were smiling and they were very happy to see them.

Jake did a "high five" at one of them. He was very surprised when the angel "high fived" him right back.

Wow!' said Jake, "Angels are really cool!"

The angel kept going down the stairs as though he had an important mission and Jake kept moving up towards the gate.

Are they not all ministering spirits, sent out to render service for the sake of those who shall inherit salvation? Hebrews 1:14 (NKJV)

When they arrived at the top, the gate was open. Jake and Jenny could not believe their eyes!

It was Jesus. Both of them gave Him the biggest hug ever!

Jesus laughed and hugged them both tightly. "Welcome!" He said, "I've been waiting for your visit."

"Wow!" said Jake, "You knew we were coming?"

Then he dreamed, and behold, a ladder was set up on the earth, and its top reached to heaven; and there the angels of God were ascending and descending on it. And behold, the Lord stood above it and said: "I am the Lord God of Abraham your father and the God of Isaac; the land on which you lie I will give to you and your descendants.
Genesis 28: 12-13 (NKJV)

"Oh yes" He said, "Would you like to look around?"

"Yes please!" They shouted in unison.

They looked at each other with big smiles on their faces.
They were talking to Jesus and, He wanted to show them Heaven!

"What do you see?" He asked.

"I see beautiful stones." Jake said, "and I see a river.
May I throw stones into the river?"

Without waiting for an answer he ran ahead and picked up
a stone. Then he tried to make it skip on the water, just like his
Dad taught him.

Jenny was embarrassed..
"Sometimes Jake gets so excited!"

Jesus smiled at her and said,
"When I was a boy I skipped
stones on the water too!"

"Really?" Jenny said as she picked up a stone. "I think these are too pretty to throw into the river. I love the colours, and how they glow in the sunlight."

Jenny put the stone in her pocket. She was not going to throw it away. She called to Jake to come back to the path.

Jesus was very patient and waited for Jake to join them.
"What do you see down the path?" He asked.

Both Jenny and Jake looked and saw the most amazing garden with flowers, trees, and a river flowing gently through it.

There was a bench right beside the river.

And the LORD God planted a garden eastward in Eden; and there he put the man whom he had formed. And a river went out of Eden to water the garden; Genesis 2:8; Genesis 2:10 (NKJV)

Jake ran ahead and climbed one of the trees. He yelled from the very top. "You can see the mountains from here!"

"Get down Jake! You're making me nervous. What if you fall?"

Jake jumped down from the top. Jenny couldn't believe her eyes.   He seemed to float down like he was able to fly.

"This place is amazing!"He said.

Jenny sat down and looked at a beautiful flower.
She was very curious.

She wanted to pick it but wasn't sure if she should.
She looked up to see Jesus. He just nodded and smiled.

As Jenny picked the flower the
most wonderful thing happened.
Another flower immediately took its
place! Nothing dies in this garden
and strangely, Jenny also heard
soft music and sounds. What is this
place she wondered?

As she looked up from the flowers, Jenny saw that Jake and Jesus were sitting on the bench by the river.

Jesus was showing Jake His hands. The scars were still there. Jake was sitting quietly for the first time.

Then, Jake hugged Jesus very tightly and said softly in a whisper, "Thank you."

He made known to us the mystery of His will, according to His kind intention which He purposed in Himself. Ephesians 1:9 (NASB)

"There is another place I would like you to see." Jesus said.

Jake and Jenny looked around them. They could only see the garden and the river. "Is it the mountain that I saw from the top of tree?" Jake asked trying to guess.

"This place has a special entrance." Jesus replied. "Look around you."

Then they saw it. The small old gate was hidden in the bushes. They could see a path leading to it. It was not well worn but you could clearly see the way.

The gate opened as they arrived.

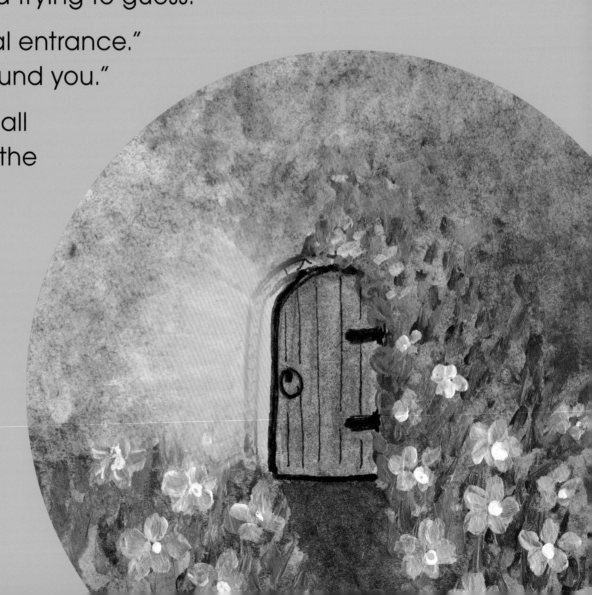

As they walked in, Jesus pointed to the shelves, "This room is called 'Destiny Scrolls'. Many want to know what is written in the book of their life, but few have come to this room."

Jake just stood there wondering if he could climb up the tall library ladders.

You saw me before I was born. Every day of my life was recorded in your book. Every moment was laid out before a single day had passed. Psalm 139:16 (NLT)

Jesus knew exactly what Jake was thinking and said, "Go ahead." There is a book here with your name on it."

Jake needed no more encouragement. He was up the ladder faster than you can say "See you later, alligator!"

There he was again, climbing and making the ladder go across the shelves. They moved effortlessly as Jake whisked back and forth.

Then Jenny saw it. She couldn't believe it! There it was in plain sight. Not hidden on a shelf. It was right there!

Best of all, it had a name on it . . . JENNY!

Jenny took the book to the bench in the garden. She saw that some of the pages in her book were empty. She began to wonder. "If this is a book about me, why can't I see everything that is going to happen in the future?"

Jesus knew what she was thinking and He replied. "The words on your pages are given to you each day, so that we can live that day together. When people want to know about things too far ahead, it makes them worry and sometimes careless. You can come here and read your book with Me every day."

"For I know the plans I have for you," declares the Lord, "plans to prosper you and not to harm you, plans to give you hope and a future." Jeremiah 29:11 (NIV)

Jenny was worried. "How do I carry around such a big book all the time?" She asked.

Jesus replied, "Jenny, this book is actually written on your heart. You can't always see it as clearly as when it is in your lap like this but you can always sit with me and I will help you to know what is written on it."

Yet God has made everything beautiful for its own time. He has planted eternity in the human heart, but even so, people cannot see the whole scope of God's work from beginning to end.
Ecclesiates 3:11 (NLT)

Jake joined them at the bench. He had found his book too.
They both seemed to understand.

"But this is the new covenant I will make with the people of Israel after those days," says the Lord. "I will put my instructions deep within them, and I will write them on their hearts. I will be their God, and they will be my people." Jeremiah 31:33 (NLT)

"Your heart often knows what your eyes can't always see."
Jesus said to them both. "This is a place in the garden that
you can come to visit Me any time."

"How can we come here again?" Jake and Jenny asked together.

"Have you forgotten so soon?" Jesus said. "Remember the ladder?
Do you remember climbing it and seeing the angels? I was at the top
waiting for you!"

"Oh yes!" Jenny said. "Jacob's ladder."

"Yes, your hearts found a pathway that your mind had hidden." Jesus said to them very softly.

"It is a mystery but in it you will find Me. When you find this pathway and travel it often, the path will become well worn and familiar. I am always waiting for you to come up to see Me. Come to Me anytime you want. Go on back now and you will see what I mean"

"Come, let us go up to the mountain of the Lord, to the house of Jacob's God. There He will teach us His ways, and we shall walk in His paths" Isaiah 2:3 (NLT)

Jake and Jenny walked back down the same path that they had travelled to the garden. They saw the gate and the stairs. The angels were still going down and up. Together, holding hands, they walked back down.

When they reached the bottom, they looked up. Jesus was standing there smiling.

They waved and called to Him, "See You again . . . soon!"

"Yes, I am the gate. Those who come in through me will be saved. They will come and go freely and will find good pastures." John 10:9 (NLT)

The next morning Jenny said excitedly, "Did you see what I saw last night Jake?"

Then. . . they both became very quiet. It had felt so real!

Jake asked, "Do you think it was just a dream? The stairs – the angels – the garden – the river – I climbed the tree – the books! Jenny, – the books! You saw them too!"

Jake was suddenly very quiet. "Oh my goodness!" He spoke in a whisper. "Jenny, look!" Jake opened his hand – it had been tightly closed and now . . .

Jenny's eyes got bigger and bigger . . . .

Then she remembered. From her pocket she took out
a stone too. . . a perfect gem stone from the path by the river.

He made known to us the mystery of His will, according to His
kind intention which He purposed in Him Ephesians 1:9 (NASB)

Just then their mom came into their room.
"Good morning my darlings. Did you sleep well?"
"Oh mom!" they said together . . . . "Heaven is REALLY real!
Would you like us to take you there?"

Dear Reader,

Jacob saw the Lord standing at the top of the ladder and that same gate is open to us today. Jesus is always there to meet us and to speak with us.

Some folk call this "ascending" and it is really a great term. The Body of Christ has been asking for the Lord to visit us, to come down when the fact is, He wants us to come up so He can show us around His Kingdom. Just like the disciple John on the Isle of Patmos heard a voice say "Come up here," (Revelation 4:1) that same request is being asked of us today.

The Lord wants to help us to see the reality of what we are created for as 'new creations in Christ,' (2 Corinthians 5:17) He wants us to walk in Kingdom of Heaven realities and to encourage us "Set our hearts on things above and not only on things of this world." (Colossians 3:2)

Scripture says we are "seated with Christ in Heavenly places" (Ephesians 2:6) yet we stay 'earth bound' like a caterpillar rather than a butterfly that has been set free to fly high.

The Kingdom Adventures of Jake and Jenny is a work of fiction. However, the truth is that the Scriptures are an access or a gateway into the world of the Kingdom that we can enter into ourselves at any time. Jacob's Ladder is one of those. (Genesis 28:16,17)

It is my hope that some of the principles that we are learning will be shared with the young as well as the young at heart. The best way to learn about a new place is not to just hear about it but to see and experience it yourself. We experience more by traveling there than just reading about it in a book.

Come with me up Jacob's Ladder. Step in by faith as a child and journey into a deeper intimacy with the Lord and to see what He would say to you personally every day. There are wonderful things written for you on your scroll.

See you in Heaven!

Helen

You will see greater things than these." And He said to him, "Most assuredly I say to you, hereafter you shall see heaven open, and the angels of God ascending and descending upon the Son of Man." John 1: 50b -51 (NKJV)